Songs
of
Fellowship

for praise and worship

Published jointly by

KINGSWAY PUBLICATIONS
and
CRUSADE FOR WORLD REVIVAL

First published 1979
Reprinted 1980

ISBN 0 86065 029 4

The arrangements are by Margaret Evans.

Printed in Great Britain for
KINGSWAY PUBLICATIONS LTD
Lottbridge Drove, Eastbourne, E. Sussex BN23 6NT and
CRUSADE FOR WORLD REVIVAL
Box 11, Walton-on-Thames, Surrey by
Richard Clay (The Chaucer Press) Ltd., Bungay, Suffolk

Contents

Contents

Praise

PSALM 104:33 I will sing to the Lord as long
as I live; I will sing praise to
my God while I have my being.

1.

As eternity begins

P. Lawson-Johnson/P. Somerville

Joyfully
Intro.

I want to sing a-bout my Je - sus, ___ I want to sing a-bout my Lord, ___ I want to tell you of His King-dom ___ and His bles - sings a - broad. ___ We are new, we are ho - ly, ___ We are washed, we are

0

2. I want to meet Him on the mountain;
   I want to stand before His throne.
   He has asked me to His table
   To share the beauty of His home.

   We are welcome, we are chosen,
   Children in His family.
   I never cease to gaze in wonder
   At what He has revealed to me.

   So, can I share with you my Jesus;
   Share with you my precious Lord.
   Let me lead you to the Kingdom.
   He is the way, He is the door.

2. Come and praise Him, royal priesthood

3. Come bless the Lord

P. Lawson-Johnson

4. Hallelujah, praise the name of the Lord

5. Happy are the people

M. Ray

Hap-py are the people ___ who have learned to acclaim You Who walk, O Lord, in the light of Your presence. ___ In Your name ___ they shall re - joice all the day long Your righteousness shall lift them up. ___

Chorus

Hal - le - lu - ia, Hal - le - lu - ia, Hal - le - lu - ia, Hal - le - lu - ia. ___

2. You are Yourself the strength in which we glory
    Through Your grace we hold our heads up high
    The Lord our God, He is our strength and shield
    The Holy One of Israel is our King.

6. Hinds' feet

P. Lawson-Johnson

Joyfully
Intro.

1. Tho' the fig tree shall not blos - som, nei-ther fruit be on the vine;

And the pro-duce of the ol - ive tree shall fail.

Chorus

Yet I will re-joice in the Lord,_____ I will re-joice in the Lord,_____ I will re-joice in the Lord, I will joy in the God of my sal -

high, _____ up-on high _____ up-on high plac - es. _____

He will make me to high _____ up-on

high _____ up-on high plac - es. _____

2. Though the fields shall yield no food,
   And the flock shall lose the fold,
   And there shall be no herd found in the stall.
   Yet, I will rejoice in the Lord,
   I will rejoice in the Lord,
   I will rejoice in the Lord,
   I will joy in the God of my salvation.

   The Lord is my strength,
   He will make my feet like hinds' feet,
   He will make me to walk, He will make me to walk
   Upon high, upon high, upon high, upon high places.

7.   I will sing unto the Lord

author unknown
arranged Margaret Evans

8.

Make a joyful noise

C. Head

Make a joy-ful noise un-to the Lord, all ye lands, all ye lands.

Make a joy-ful noise un-to the Lord, all ye lands, all ye lands.

Come be-fore Him with sing-ing, Come be-fore Him with joy.

Make a joy-ful noise un-to the Lord, all ye lands, all ye lands.

2. Open your hearts before Him now.
Give Him your praise, give Him your praise.
Open your hearts before Him now.
Give Him your praise, give Him your praise.
Come before Him with singing, *etc.*

9.
Praise You, Lord
(Isaiah 53; 61:1-3; Philippians 2:5-11)

Capo 3 (C)

With majesty

N. Rose

Praise You, — Lord, for the won-der of Your heal - ing.

Praise You, — Lord, for Your love so free - ly given,

out - pour-ing a - noin-ting, flow-ing in to — heal our wounds.

Praise You, — Lord, for Your love for — me.

2. Praise You, Lord, for Your gift of liberation.
   Praise You, Lord, You have set the captives free;
   The chains that bind are broken by the sharpness of Your sword,
   Praise You, Lord, You gave Your life for me.

3. Praise You, Lord, You have born the depths of sorrow.
   Praise You, Lord, for Your anguish on the tree;
   The nails that tore Your body and the pain that tore Your soul.
   Praise You, Lord, Your tears, they fell for me.

4. Praise You, Lord, You have turned our thorns to roses.
   Glory, Lord, as they bloom upon Your brow.
   The path of pain is hallowed, for Your love has made it sweet,
   Praise You, Lord, and may I love You now.

10. Sing unto the Lord a new song

M. Ray

Worship

REVELATION 5:12 Worthy is the Lamb that was slain to receive power . . . and honour and glory and blessing.

11.

But ye are washed

P. Simmons

Worshipfully

But ye are washed,_____ But ye are sanc-

-ti-fied; But ye are jus-ti-fied_____ in the

name_____ of the Lord Je-

sus, of the Lord Je-sus, And by the

Spi-rit of_____ our God._____

12. Fellowship sweet

M. Wilkinson/R. Turner

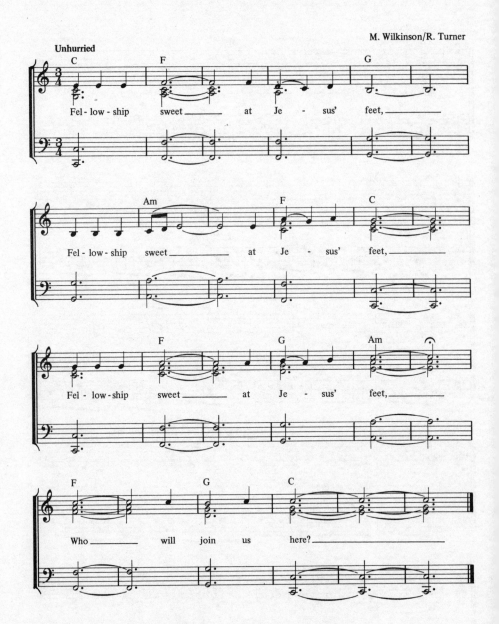

2. Love we share when Jesus is there, *(three times)*
    . . . Who will join us there?

3. Money we share when Jesus is there, *etc.*

4. Bread and wine, with Jesus we'll dine, *etc.*

5. We love to sing to Jesus our King, *etc.*

13. Hosanna to the Son of David

M. Ford

With majesty

You are the King of Glo-ry. You are the Prince of Peace. You are the Lord of heav'n and earth. You're the Son of righteousness. An-gels bow down be - fore_You Wor - ship and a - dore, for You have the words of e - ter-nal life,_You are Je-sus Christ the Lord.____ Ho - san-na to the Son of Da-vid!____ Ho - san-na to the King of __ Kings! Glo-ry in the high-est hea - ven, for Je - sus the Mes-si - ah reigns.

14.

It's so good, my Lord

Capo 3 (G)

M. Ray

It's so good, my Lord, _____ Liv - ing my life ___ in You. _____ For Your yoke is ea - sy and Your bur - den is light _____ Feels so Joy of for - give - ness, _____

2. Knowing I'm loved, Lord, standing in Your grace,
Reigning in life, running the race.

15. I will magnify Your name, O Lord

D. Bolton

2. I will magnify Your name, O Lord, Hallelujah!
I will drink of the well of Your love, Hallelujah!
With instrument and with voice, Hallelujah!
My spirit in You shall rejoice, Hallelujah!

3. I will magnify Your name, O Lord, Hallelujah!
I will drink of the well of Your love, Hallelujah!
With the timbrel and the dance, Hallelujah!
My love for You I shall express, Hallelujah!

4. I will magnify Your name, O Lord, Hallelujah!
I will drink of the well of Your love, Hallelujah!
I will worship You to the end of my days, Hallelujah!
With a heart that is full of praise, Hallelujah!

16. Jesus, how lovely You are

Worshipfully
Chorus

D. Bolton

Je - sus,___ how love-ly You are.___ You are so gen-tle so pure and kind.___

You___ shine as the morn-ing star.___ Je - sus, how love-ly You are.___

Fine

1. Hal - le-lu - jah, Je - sus is my Lord and King.___

D.C. al Fine

Hal - le - lu - jah, Je - sus is___ my ev - 'ry - thing.

2. Hallelujah, Jesus died and rose again;
   Hallelujah, Jesus forgave all my sin.

3. Hallelujah, Jesus is meek and lowly;
   Hallelujah, Jesus is pure and holy.

4. Hallelujah, Jesus is the Bridegroom;
   Hallelujah, Jesus will take His Bride soon.

17. Lord, I feel

D. Bolton

Smoothly
Chorus

Lord, _____ I feel _____ Your sweet pre - sence where ev - er I go. _____ Lord, _____ I _____ feel _____ Your sweet pre - sence where ev - er I go. _____ go. _____

To verse | *Last time* | *Fine*

2.   If I should fail and feel despair,
      You lift me above all my care.

3.   Lord, I love You and I know that You love me,
      I feel Your love embracing me.

18.

My peace

K. Routledge

Gently ♪= 120

1. My peace ___ I give ___ un-to you, ___ It's a peace ___ that the world ___ can-not give, ___ It's a peace ___ that the world ___ can-not un - der - stand. ___ Peace to know, peace to live. ___ My peace ___ I give ___ un-to you. ___

2. My joy I give unto you,
It's a joy that the world cannot give,
It's a joy that the world cannot understand.
Joy to know, joy to live.
My joy I give unto you.

3. My love I give unto you,
It's a love that the world cannot give,
It's a love that the world cannot understand.
Love to know, love to live.
My love I give unto you.

19. Take My yoke upon you

F. Chedgey

20. Unto Thee do I lift my eyes

P. Simmons

The Kingdom

HEBREWS 2:9   But we see Jesus . . . crowned with
glory and honour . . .

ISAIAH 9:7   Of the increase of His government
and peace there shall be no end.

21.   The Church of God

M. Ray

The Church of God is not stee-ples,_____ house meet-ings or ca-the-drals._____ But the Church of God is peo-ple_____ whose hearts have be-come the dwell-ing place of God in the Spi-rit;_____ Walk-ing in the light with God and one an-oth-er, be-ing built to-ge-ther_____

22.

Come, walk with me

P. Ive

Lightly with pace

Come, walk with me round the walls of the ci - ty, See what the King has been

build-ing so well. Put down your tools rest a - while from your la - bours,

Lift up your eyes, lift your hands, come and see. Come, dance with me round the

walls of the ci - ty, Let us give glo - ry to Je - sus our King.

2. You are the stones, which His love is now shaping,
    Lives being made into praise for our God,
    See the pure stone that the builders rejected
    Now the foundation, the glory of God.
    Come dance with me, we're the stones of that city,
    Giving the glory to Jesus our King.

23. For I'm building a people of power

Brightly

D. Richards

For I'm build-ing a peo-ple of pow-er___ And I'm build-ing a peo-ple of praise, That will move thro' this land by My Spi-rit,___ And will glo-ri-fy My prec-ious Name. Build Your Church, Lord, Make us strong, Lord, Join our hearts, Lord, through Your Son. Make us one, Lord, in Your Bo-dy, In the King-dom of Your Son.___

24.   Jesus is changing me

A. Revell

2. Then shall the blessing of the Lord come down,
When we give all to Him;
And we shall go forth in holiness
Delighting ourselves in God.

25.

Love is waiting here

P. Lawson-Johnson

Come, all you thirsty
na - tions,___ Come to the ri - ver side.___
If your foun-tains have run dry then come and be sa - tis-
fied.___

2. How many sons in glory
   Only the Father knows;
   How many will be touched with love
   As the wind of the Spirit blows.

   How many have found freedom,
   How many have found joy,
   Knowing the love that comes from Jesus
   Nothing can destroy,
   Nothing can destroy.

   Come through to Jesus,
   The Lord is waiting for you.
   Come through to Jesus,
   The water is so clear,
   Love is waiting here
   A stream of everlasting Life.

26.   Lord, please make Your people one

A. Woodroffe/C. Head

2. All around the kingdoms fall,
But we hear our Father call —
You are safe, My children, with Me.
Show My love, for I want the world to see.

3. Lord, You're making Your people one,
And answering the prayer of Your dear Son,
That the world may see that we are one,
And give the glory unto You.

27.
Sweet fellowship

With pace

R. Wilson

Sweet fel-low-ship, Je-sus in the midst. Life blos-soms in the Church, men by men are blessed When Je-sus is in the midst. I've ne-ver known a time like this Feel the spi-rit with-in me rise, Come and see what God is do-ing, Lord, we love You.

Fine

D.C. al Fine

2. Peace and harmony — Jesus reigning here;
The Church moves at His command,
No room for doubt or fear
For Jesus is reigning here.

I've never known a time like this
Feel the spirit within me rise.
Come and see what God is doing,
Lord, we love You. . . .

3. Sweet fellowship, Jesus in the midst,
Life blossoms in the Church.
Men by men are blessed
When Jesus is in the midst.

Prayer

MATTHEW 7:7   Ask, and it shall be given to you;
seek, and you shall find; knock,
and it shall be opened to you.

28.

Abba Father

Capo 3 (G)

D. Bilbrough

29. Ask and it shall be given

A. Woodroffe/C. Head

Ask, and it shall be gi - ven un - to you. Ask, and it shall be ____ done. ____ As we pray in the name of our Lord Je - sus Christ; ____ As we

pray   in   the   name   of   God's   Son._____

_____   God   has   placed   with -

in   our___   hearts _____ A   know - ledge__ of

His ___ per - fect   will, _____   And

30. Father, I place into Your hands

Capo 1 (E)

Gently

J. Hewer

Fa-ther, I place in-to Your hands the things I can-not do.

Fa-ther, I place in-to Your hands___ the things that I've been through.

Fa-ther, I place in-to Your hands the way that I should go, For I

know I al-ways can trust You.___

2. Father, I place into Your hands
My friends and family.
Father, I place into Your hands
The things that trouble me.
Father, I place into Your hands
The person I would be,
For I know I always can trust You.

3. Father, we love to see Your face,
We love to hear Your voice,
Father, we love to sing your praises
And in Your name rejoice,
Father, we love to walk with You
And in Your presence rest,
For I know I always can trust You.

4. Father, I want to be with You
And do the things You do.
Father, I want to speak the words
That You are speaking too.
Father, I want to love the ones
That You will draw to You,
For I know that I am one with You.

31.
Jesus take me as I am

Capo 4 (C)

D. Bryant

Je-sus take me as I am,————
I can come no oth-er way.————
Take me deep-er in to You,————
Make my flesh life melt a - way.————

32. More of You

M. Ray

Peacefully

Lord, I want to know More of You.

Lord, I want to know so much more of You; As a

hart longs for the flow-ing stream so my heart longs for You. Re-

veal Your-self, Lead me on in-to know-ing more of You.

Thanksgiving

EPHESIANS 5:20   Always giving thanks for all things
in the name of our Lord Jesus Christ.

33.

He alone

C. White

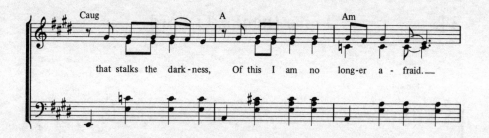

that stalks the dark-ness, Of this I am no long-er a-fraid. ___

He a-lone ___ is my re - fuge, I am no long-er a-fraid. ___

2. A thousand may fall at our right hand;
   We stand alone amidst disaster.
   Evil will not touch us;
   From all we will be delivered.

3. We have made the Lord our refuge,
   We have chosen Him for shelter.
   His angels keep us from falling,
   In His hands He bears us up.

4. Because you cleave to Me in love,
   I will deliver you.
   I will protect you
   Because you know My name.

5. When you call, I will answer.
   I will be with you in trouble;
   You will know your joy fulfilled
   And see My salvation.

34.

I give thanks, O Lord

P. Lawson-Johnson

For Thy stead-fast love and faith-ful - ness, Thy stead-fast love and

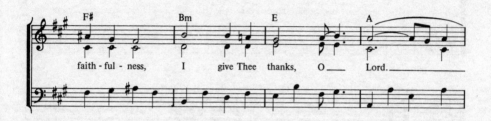

faith - ful - ness, I give Thee thanks, O ___ Lord. _____

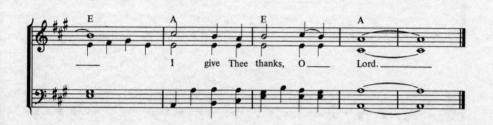

___ I give Thee thanks, O ___ Lord. _____

2. For Thou hast exalted above everything
   Thy name and Thy word on high,
   On the day I called, Thou didst answer me,
   My strength of soul Thou didst increase
   My strength of soul Thou didst increase.

3. Thou dost stretch out Thy hand against my foes,
   Thy right hand delivers me.
   The Lord will fulfil His purpose for me,
   Thy steadfast love endures for ever
   Thy steadfast love endures for ever.

35.

I'm forgiven

Capo 2 (G)

M. Ray

2. Living in Your presence, Lord, is life itself.
   I'm forgiven, I'm forgiven.
   With the past behind, grace for today
     and a hope to come.
   I'm forgiven, I'm forgiven.

36. I'm saved by the grace of God

I. Traynor

With feeling
Verse

I'm saved _____ by the grace of God, _____

Root-ed _____ and fixed in love, _____ and I'm fi - nished _____

_____ with my old life. _____ I'm a - live _____ in a brand new

Chorus

way _____ And it's ea - sy to live now, _____ I've gi - ven my

all, _____ Sur - rend-ered ____ ev - 'ry - thing to You. _____

_____ I have no rights on my life, _____

_____ O Je - sus, _____ You are my Lord. _____

2. I know I have died to sin,
   Baptised into His glorious death;
   I've been raised up into newness of life,
   I'm no longer a slave to sin.

3. I live now by the law of God
   Written on my heart,
   And the Spirit and my brothers
   Are showing me where I've got to change.

4. My life is hid with Christ in God,
   I know I am secure
   And nothing can separate me
   From the love which is in Christ.

37.   My life is really blessed

My life is real-ly blessed be-cause I know the love of God

And I can be so free to live and move within that

love; Part of His fa-mi-ly, Liv-ing in vic-to-ry, Se-cure in know-ing that Je-sus has got ev-'ry-thing in hand.

Verse

Some-times I won-der if I'll e - ver get through,

And I see my life's in need of chang-ing,

But though He dis - ci - plines, it's al - ways in love,

And so with con - fid-ence I say.

D.C. al Fine

2. So I'm really happy to be walking with God
   Knowing His care from day to day,
   He is the answer to my every desire,
   And so with confidence I say...

38. My Lord, You are so good to me

Capo 3 (G)

P. & D. Roe

39. Jesus, thank You, Jesus

F. Chedgey

With Simplicity

Je - sus,_____ Thank You, Je - sus,_____ for all You
are to me, for all the things You do._____ But I
thank You_____ most of all, Lord,_____ For show-ing
me how much I mean to You._____

40. Thank You, Jesus, for Your love to me

A. Revell

Thank You, Je - sus, _____ for Your love to me. _____

Thank You, Je - sus, _____ for Your grace so free. _____

I'll lift my voice to praise Your name, Praise You a-gain and a-

gain. You are ev - 'ry - thing, _____ You are my Lord. _____

41. Why should I lose my first love?

Capo 5 (C)

I. Traynor

With warmth

Why should I lose my first love, When

He's been so grac - ious ___ un-to me? ___ He's dis-

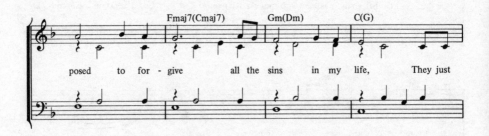

posed to for - give all the sins in my life, They just

melt at the whis-per ___ of His word. ___

Fine

O the na-ture of that smile on His for-giv-ing

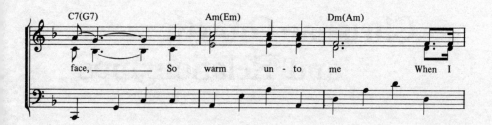

face, ___ So warm un-to me When I

need-ed so much grace. ___ 3. I

2.   Why should I lose my first love
     When I've seen Him so full of grace and truth.
     Why run away from that blessed ground
     Where I first met a love so warm and deep.

3.   I love Him more now after I've sinned
     For I've found out what He is really like.
     He's a God of such love, He'll forgive and forget
     So I can put my full trust in Him now.

Christian Growth and Relationships

EPHESIANS 2:22   We are being built together into
a dwelling of God in the Spirit.

42.

Do not strive

G. Kendrick

2. We'll let You have Your way among us,
   We'll not strive, we'll not strive. *Repeat.*
   For Yours is the power and the glory
   For ever and ever the same.
   We'll let You have Your way among us,
   We'll not strive, we'll not strive.

3. Let My peace rule within your hearts,
   Do not strive, do not strive. *Repeat.*
   For Mine is the power and the glory
   For ever and ever the same.
   Let My peace rule within your hearts,
   Do not strive, do not strive.

4. We'll let Your peace rule within our hearts,
   We'll not strive, we'll not strive. *Repeat.*
   For yours. . . *etc.*

43. Arise, arise

Capo 3 (C)

Y. Gale/M. Smith

I have loved You with an ev - er - last - ing love____

____ And have cont - in - ued My faith-ful - ness__ to you._____ A-

- gain I will build __ you and you shall be built, And

I will be your God, says the Lord._____ So a -

Copyright © 1977 Thank You Music

2.   Again you'll adorn yourself with the timbrels,
And go forth in the dance of the merrymakers,
So plant your vineyards and you'll enjoy the fruit
And I will be your God says the Lord.
So arise, arise and let's go up to Zion.
Arise, arise and let's go up to Zion.
Arise to the Lord our God.

44.

Be kind

P. & D. Roe

Lif:ingly with steady pace
Chorus

If there be an-y love be-tween us, let's keep this in mind:
Be kind, be kind,
And if there's an-y un-der-stand-ing be-tween us let's keep this in
mind, Be kind, Be
kind, Be kind.

Verse

For a new com - mand-ment _____ I give un - to you, That you

love one an - oth - er ev - en as I have loved you.

Then all will know ____ that you are My dis - ci - ples _____ If

you love ____ one an - oth - er. _____ So if there's

2. Love one another — that's what Jesus said,
    So let's be kind and tenderhearted —
        to our brother who is our friend.
    Let's live together — working out life in love,
    Let's be sure our love endures — to the end.

3. Sometimes love can hurt us —
        and the pain of the truth is real,
    But let's remember that our Father —
        is building His people with steel,
    We are sons and daughters — children of the King,
    So let's lay down our lives and feelings
        for our friends.

45. Bind us together

Easy waltz feel

B. Gillman

Chorus

Bind us to-ge-ther, Lord, Bind us to-ge-ther with

cords that can-not be bro - ken.

Bind us to - ge - ther, Lord, Bind us to - ge - ther,

Bind us to - ge - ther with love.

Verse

1. There is on - ly one God._____

There is on - ly one King._____

There is on - ly one Bo - dy._____

D.C. al Fine

That is why we sing._____

2. Made for the glory of God,
Purchased by His precious Son.
Born with the right to be clean,
For Jesus the victory has won. . . .

3. You are the family of God.
You are the promise divine.
You are God's chosen desire.
You are the glorious new wine. . . .

46.   If your heart is right with my heart

Capo 5 (C)

G. Perrins

If your heart is right with my __ heart __ give me your hand. __

If your heart is right with my heart __ give me your hand. __

The right hand of fel-low - ship, The right hand of co - ve - nant; If your

heart is right with my __ heart __ give me your hand. __

2. If your heart is right with my heart,
Then we shall love;
If your heart is right with my heart,
Then we shall love.
We shall love in word and deed,
And be open to each need;
If your heart is right with my heart
Then we shall love.

3. If your heart is right with my heart,
We shall be one;
If your heart is right with my heart,
We shall be one.
One in heart and mind and soul,
One in purpose and in goal;
If your heart is right with my heart
We shall be one.

47. Jesus, stand among us

Capo 3 (C)

G. Kendrick

Je - sus, stand a - mong us___ at the meet - ing of our lives, Be our sweet a - gree - ment___ at the meet - ing of our eyes; O, Je - sus, we love You so we ga - ther here, Join our hearts in un - i - ty___ and take a - way___ our fear.___

2.   So to You we're gathering out of each and every land,
      Christ the love between us at the joining of our hands;
      O, Jesus, we love You, so we gather here,
      Join our hearts in unity and take away our fear.

48. Let us open up ourselves

P. Barton

Flowing
Chorus

Let us o - pen up our - selves to one an - oth - er with-out fear of be -ing hurt or turned a - way;____ For we need to con-fess our weak-ness-es,__ To be co-vered by our bro-ther's love, To be real and learn our true i - den - ti - ty.____ *Fine*

Verse For we are all a part of one an - oth - er,____ We

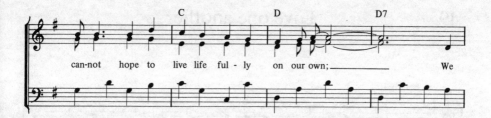

can-not hope to live life ful-ly on our own;_____ We

each pos-sess a prec-ious part_ of our Fa-ther's na - ture, And to

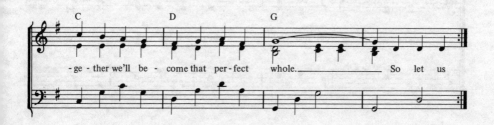

-ge - ther we'll be - come that per-fect whole._____ So let us

2. And God shall surely build His living temple
    Of people set completely free,
    Loving and appreciating one another,
    Enjoying life in its entirety.

3. Many shall be drawn to us and wonder
    At the peace and the love and the joy that will never die;
    They will drink from that stream of living water
    Flowing out from the fulness of our lives.

4. So help us to understand each other in a new and living way,
    Not just accepting words that are spoken in themselves,
    But by speaking more freely and listening more clearly
    We shall understand the spirit that's within.

49.

Love one another

N. Rose

Easy Waltz

Love one an-oth-er as I have loved you,____ Be right-eous, be ho-ly, in all that you do. Just seek Me, lis-ten to____ Me with all your heart, fol-low Me and I pro-mise you shall____ not____ fall.____ And I pro-mise you shall____ not____ fall.____ So

50. We are being built into a temple

51. We are moving on

Capo 1 (D)

Flowing pace

We are mov-ing on in-to a deep ap-pre-ci-

a-tion—— of the love which flows from Fa-ther out to

ev-'ry child of God, ———— Of the grace with which He

hand-les ev-'ry mi-nute sit-u-a-tion, How He

wants the best for ev - 'ry - one who gives to Him his

Chorus

all. _____ Grace it seems is all He has, and

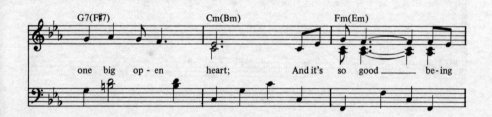

one big op - en heart; And it's so good _____ be - ing

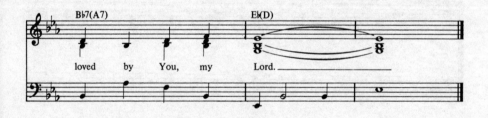

loved by You, my Lord. _____

2. We will know and understand
    His purposes more clearly,
    O, the mystery of the things He does
    In making us more whole.
    With His love He woos us,
    By His grace He sets us free;
    We can only trust Him
    And just hold on to His hand.

52.

We are never alone

A. Woodroffe

Easily
Chorus

We are nev-er a - lone. God has giv - en us His fa - mi - ly. We are nev-er a - lone, In God's fa - mi - ly we have se - cu - ri - ty.

Verse

1. In the moun - tains or in the val - leys,
When things go right, When things go wrong,
It's good to know We have God's fa - mi - ly,
A fa - mi - ly where we know we be - long.

2. As we share and as we live,
As we receive and as we give,
We will build up
Each other until we all attain
The fulness of the stature of Christ.

53. We shall be as one

J. Parsons

Smoothly

We shall be as one, _____ We shall be as one, _____

He the Fa - ther of us all, _____ We His cho - sen sons; _____

And by His com - mand _____ Take each oth - er's hand, _____

Live our lives in u - ni - ty, _____ We shall be as one.

2. We shall be as one,
   We shall be as one;
   And by this shall all men know
   Of the work He has done.
   Love will take us on
   Through His precious Son;
   Love of Him who first loved us
   We shall be as one.

Index of titles and first lines

(First line where different from title
is shown in *italics*)

Songs of Fellowship Recordings

Many of the songs in this book are featured on these two albums issued by
Kingsway Music:

A NEW SONG   *Dove 47*
Songs include: Abba Father/ Bind us together/
Jesus stand among us/For I'm building a people of
power/Jesus is changing me/Sing unto the Lord a
new song/*and ten others.*

CITY OF GOD   *Dove 53*
Songs include: Come and praise Him, royal priesthood/
Thank You, Jesus, for Your love to me/My life is really
blessed/Jesus take me as I am/We shall be as one/I will
sing unto the Lord/*and eleven others.*

Further information can be obtained from your usual supplier.